Jim's Junk

and

Fix It

D0101345

'Jim's Junk' and 'Fix It'
An original concept by Jenny Jinks
© Jenny Jinks

Illustrated by Srimalie Bassani

Published by MAVERICK ARTS PUBLISHING LTD
Studio 3A, City Business Centre, 6 Brighton Road,
Horsham, West Sussex, RH13 5BB
© Maverick Arts Publishing Limited May 2019
+44 (0)1403 256941

A CIP catalogue record for this book is available at the British Library.

ISBN 978-1-84886-438-2

www.maverickbooks.co.uk

Pink

This book is rated as: Pink Band (Guided Reading)
This story is decodable at Letters and Sounds Phase 2.

Jim's Junk

and

Fix It

By
Jenny Jinks

Illustrated by
Srimalie Bassani

The Letter J

Trace the lower and upper case letter with a finger. Sound out the letter.

*Down,
around,
lift,
dot*

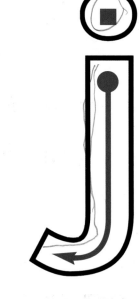

*Down,
around,
lift,
cross*

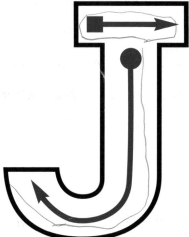

Some words to familiarise:

junk   Jim   go-kart

High-frequency words:

in a the it put is this

Tips for Reading 'Jim's Junk'

- *Practise the words listed above before reading the story.*
- *If the reader struggles with any of the other words, ask them to look for sounds they know in the word. Encourage them to sound out the words and help them read the words if necessary.*
- *After reading the story, ask the reader what Jim made from all the bits of junk.*

Fun Activity

Have a go at making new things from cardboard boxes!

Ben put it in the bin.

Dan put it in the bin.

Lil put it in the bin.

Jim got the bits.

Bang! Bang!

Tap! Tap!

The Letter F

Trace the lower and upper case letter with a finger. Sound out the letter.

*Around,
down,
lift,
cross*

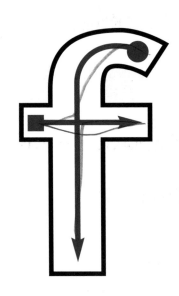

*Down,
lift,
cross,
lift,
cross*

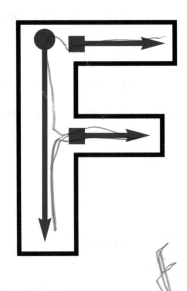

Some words to familiarise:

fix   Bot   car

High-frequency words:

has   a   it

Tips for Reading 'Fix It'

- *Practise the words listed above before reading the story.*

- *If the reader struggles with any of the other words, ask them to look for sounds they know in the word. Encourage them to sound out the words and help them read the words if necessary.*

- *After reading the story, ask the reader what happened to Bot in the end.*

Fun Activity

What else could you do with a robot?

Ben has a ted.

Bot can fix it.

Ella has a net.

Bot can fix it.

Meg has a car.

Bot can fix it.

Al has a bat.

Bot can fix it.

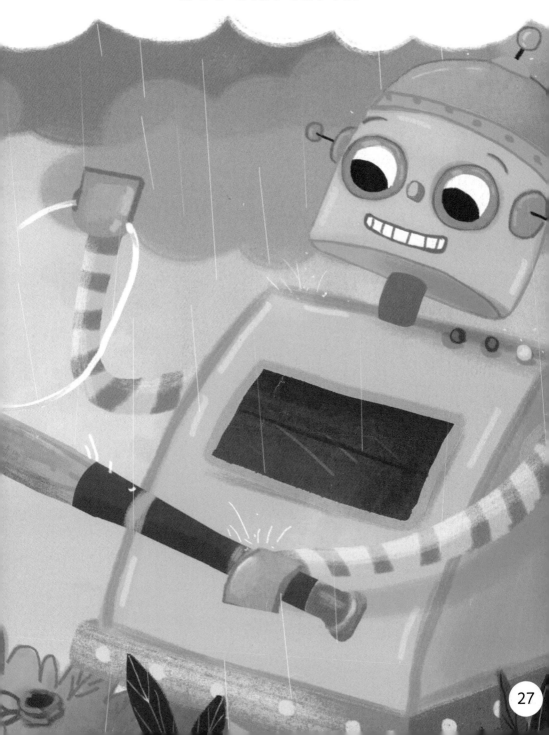

But who can fix Bot?

Book Bands for Guided Reading

The Institute of Education book banding system is a scale of colours that reflects the various levels of reading difficulty. The bands are assigned by taking into account the content, the language style, the layout and phonics. Word, phrase and sentence level work is also taken into consideration.

Maverick Early Readers are a bright, attractive range of books covering the pink to white bands. All of these books have been book banded for guided reading to the industry standard and edited by a leading educational consultant.

To view the whole Maverick Readers scheme, visit our website at

www.maverickearlyreaders.com

Or scan the QR code above to view our scheme instantly!